It's another Quality Book from CGP

This book is for 7-11 year olds.

It contains lots of tricky questions designed
to make you sweat — because that's the only
way you'll get any better.

It's also got some daft bits in to try and make
the whole experience at least vaguely
entertaining for you.

What CGP is all about

Our sole aim here at CGP is to produce the highest quality
books — carefully written, immaculately presented and
dangerously close to being funny.

Then we work our socks off to get them out to you
— at the cheapest possible prices.

Contents

Section Three — Shapes and Solids

Section Four — Measurement

Section Five — Handling Data

Answers

Published by Coordination Group Publications Ltd
Illustrated by Ruso Bradley, Chris Dennett, Lex Ward and Ashley Tyson

Contributors:
Chris Dennett
June Hall
Mark Haslam
Paul Jordin
Sharon Keeley
Simon Little
Chris Oates
Glenn Rogers
Kate Stevens
Tim Wakeling

ISBN: 978 1 84762 185 6

Groovy website: www.cgpbooks.co.uk

Printed by Elanders Hindson Ltd, Newcastle upon Tyne.
Clipart sources: CorelDRAW® and VECTOR.

Number Stuff

Q1   **Write these words as numbers:**

a) **Twenty-six** ....

b) **Seventy-three** ....

c) **Eight hundred and sixty** ....

d) **Five thousand seven hundred and ninety-two** ....

e) **Twenty-seven thousand and fifty-two** ....

f) **Four thousand one hundred and fourteen** ....

g) **Mr Lucky won three hundred and fourteen pounds on the Lottery. Write this in the space on his cheque.**

Royal Bank of CGP   Today

PAY   Mr. U. N. Lucky

Three hundred and fourteen pounds   £ [_____]

Signature L. O Terry

His friend Mrs V. Lucky won forty-two thousand six hundred and seventy-three pounds and twenty-nine pence on the Lottery.
Write this amount in the space on her cheque.

Royal Bank of CGP   Today

PAY   Mrs V. Lucky

Forty-two thousand six hundred and   £ [_____]

seventy-three pounds and twenty-nine pence

Signature L. O Terry

Q2   **Write these numbers as words:**

a) **27**   ....

b) **507**   ....

c) **3824**   ....

d) **63 492**   ....

e) **245 094**   ....

f) **372 603**   ....

Number Stuff

Q3 Write out these groups of numbers in order from <u>smallest</u> to <u>largest</u>:

a) 612   804   197   450   372   463

..............., ..., ..., ..., ..., ...

b) 86   402   2123   3860   553   75

..............., ..., ..., ..., ..., ...

c) 1879   1726   1680   1832   1724   1797

..............., ..., ..., ..., ..., ...

Q4 These are the telephone numbers of all Dirk's friends.
Put the numbers in order from <u>largest</u> to <u>smallest</u>.

Arnold 18659
T.J. 21056
Francine 18704
Beryl 21295
Cheryl 18468
Terence 21454
Nicolas 21071
Paris 18237

......................, ..., ..., ...,

......................, ..., ..., ...

Adding

Q1 Do these questions <u>without</u> a calculator and as quickly as you can. Write the answers in the spaces provided:

a) 6 + 8 = ...

b) 25 + 14 = ...

c) 34 + 72 = ...

d) 238 + 56 = ...

e) 529 + 172 = ...

f) 213 + 2513 = ...

Q2 Now try these:

a)   63
    + 32
    _____

b)   75
    + 48
    _____

c)   528
    + 196
    _____

Q3 What are the missing numbers?

a) 37 + ... = 89

b) 63 + ... = 92

c) 236 + ... = 305

Q4 Some ice boxes in a warehouse contain the following numbers of the brand new 'Rhino-on-a-stick' ice lolly.

62	218	894	42
361	1283	59	732
54	745	29	319

Select the three boxes that contain the most lollies. What is the total in these three boxes? Put your answer in the shaded box.

			Total

Select the three boxes that contain the least number of lollies. What is the total in these three boxes? Put your answer in the shaded box.

			Total

Subtracting

Q1   Work out the following subtraction sums <u>without</u> a calculator:

no calculators!!

a) 36 – 13 = ...

b) 45 – 23 = ...

c) 89 – 24 = ...

d) 25 – 8 = ...

e) 80 – 42 = ...

f) 72 – 19 = ...

g)   687
    – 235
    ——

h)   754
    – 538
    ——

i)   843
    – 516
    ——

j)   634
    – 98
    ——

k)   908
    – 325
    ——

l)   650
    – 317
    ——

m)   830
    – 293
    ——

n)   700
    – 248
    ——

Q2   What are the missing numbers?

a) 37 – .... = 20

b) 97 – .... = 17

c) 230 – .... = 110

d) 157 – .... = 82

e) 458 – .... = 294

f) 982 – .... = 13

Q3   At the beginning of the day a supermarket had 462 "Cod Man" toys. After the release of the film 'Cod Man and Halibut Boy' the toys were in great demand. By the end of the day 285 had been sold.

How many were left?   ....

Q4   Scafell Pike is 979m high. Ben Nevis is 1344m high.

What is the difference in height between the two mountains?

....

Negative Numbers

Q1   **Complete all the positive and negative numbers on the number line below.**

0

Q2   **Put the following lists of numbers in the correct order, starting with the smallest first.**

a)   -1, -11, -8, -2, -9   ....../ ....../ ....../ ....../ .....

b)   -10, -4, 1, -7, 13, -9, -2, .../ ....../ ....../ ....../ ....../ ....../ .....

c)   0, -12, -19, 12, 2, -5, -8, 6, .../ ....../ ....../ ....../ ....../ ....../ ....../ .....

Q3   **For each of the following questions there is space given for you to draw your own number line.**

a)   **A mountaineering chicken half way up Snowdon is a chilly -50°C. A chicken further down the mountain in a farmhouse is a roasting 100°C.**

(tip — you don't have to put all the points on the number line)

What is the difference in temperature between the two?   ....°C.

....

b)   **The temperature of a penguin on an iceberg in the Antarctic is -18°C. The temperature of a penguin hiding in a biscuit tin in London is 26°C.**

What is the difference in temperature between the two?   ....°C.

....

Multiplication

Q1 The world is being invaded by alien robots, but do not fear because two superheroes are here to save the day...

HAAAAAAYYYYYAAAA!!

a) 'Super-Karate-Chop-Man' is the first on the scene. With his sensational skill he manages to chop 24 robots every minute.

> If he manages to keep going for 10 minutes how many robots will he chop?

....

b) 'Super-Karate-Chop-Man' is getting tired, but do not fear, 'Man-With-Big-Mallet' is here. He has the strength of 10 DIY enthusiasts and can bash 53 robot aliens every minute.

> If he keeps smashing the robots for 27 minutes how many robots will he crush?

....

Q2 Multiply the following <u>without</u> a calculator:

a) $23 \times 2 =$ ....   b) $40 \times 3 =$ ....   c) $53 \times 4 =$ ....

d) $13 \times 5 =$ ....   e) $25 \times 4 =$ ....   f) $42 \times 3 =$ ....

g) 13
   × 5
 ─────

h) 54
   × 3
 ─────

i) 75
   × 5
 ─────

j) 93
   × 4
 ─────

k) 308
   × 4
 ─────

l) 825
   × 3
 ─────

m) 346
   × 5
 ─────

n) 286
   × 6
 ─────

Division

Q1 Divide the following <u>without</u> a calculator:

a) $20 \div 2$ ....

b) $21 \div 3$ ....

c) $40 \div 4$ ....

d) $24 \div 8$ ....

e) $15 \div 3$ ....

f) $42 \div 7$ ....

g) $5\overline{)225}$

h) $3\overline{)999}$

i) $8\overline{)640}$

j) $3\overline{)93}$

k) $5\overline{)310}$

l) $9\overline{)198}$

m) $5\overline{)300}$

n) $6\overline{)324}$

o) $7\overline{)343}$

Q2 You can use a calculator for these questions.

Action hero Mambo Moose ('the moose with no mercy') has just finished the filming for his latest movie. Due to his unique acting style he managed to complete the entire movie saying only four words.

a) If Mambo Moose gets paid £549 376 for the movie how much money does he get per word? ....

b) The four words he said were "Eat antler dirt bag".

How much did he get paid per letter?

....

c) If the four words in the movie had been "briefly savour existentialist philosophy" how much would he have got paid per letter?

....

d) Mambo Moose's wife, Bamby Anderson, likes to buy shoes.

If each pair costs £512 how many pairs can she buy with the £549 376 Mambo got for the movie?

....

8

Using Calculations

Q1 **Fill in the missing digits:**

a) $9 \times \boxed{\,|\,2} = 288$

b) $213 \times \boxed{} = 852$

c) $\boxed{\,|\,6\,|\,1} \times 3 = 783$

d) $7 \times \boxed{\,|\,8\,|\,} = 3367$

Q2 The office robots made by Cybernoid General Production Ltd weigh 40 kg and cost £12 000 each.

a) The robotics department of Julian's Organic Veg Ltd has £90 000 to spend on new robots.

How many office robots could they buy?

....

Mrs Bobbins has bought 52 office robots.
Her van can carry up to 625 kg.

b) **How many robots can Mrs Bobbins carry in her van?**

....

c) **How many trips will she need to make in the van to get all robots home?**

....

Q3 **Work out the following:**

a) $20 \div (2 + 2) =$ ....

b) $(5 - 2) \times 3 =$ ....

c) $4 \times (10 + 5) =$ ....

d) $18 \div (3 + 3) =$ ....

e) $(18 \div 3) + 3 =$ ....

f) $(11 - 7) \times (4 + 5) =$ ....

Decimals

Q1 Write the following as decimals, using numbers......

a) Two point seven ....

b) Fourteen point eight ....

c) Twenty point nine ....

d) Thirty-three point two ....

Q2 Write these fractions as decimals. The first one has been done for you:

a) One tenth 0.1

b) Three tenths ....

c) $\frac{5}{10}$ ....

d) $\frac{8}{10}$ ....

Q3 John has £2.12, Philip has £2.21 and Gordon has £2.02. Who has the most money?

....

Q4 Lisa's time for a sprint race was 12.32 seconds. Kate's time was 12.34 seconds. Who ran fastest?

....

Q5 Fill in the missing lengths.

a)

........cm

101.9cm

75.9cm

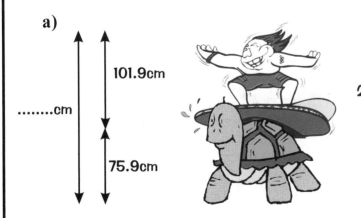

b)

101.9cm

246.7cm

........cm

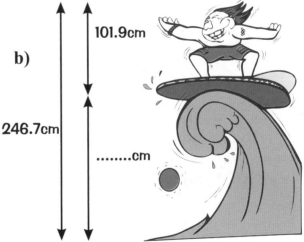

When adding decimals remember to start at the right and add each digit. If it gets to ten or more, you carry the 1 over to the next column to the left ...

Rounding Off

Q1   Give these amounts to the nearest hundred pounds.

a) £419 ....

b) £754 ....

c) £749 ....

d) £1679 ....

e) £94 ....

f) £24 ....

Q2   The average vacuum cleaner sucks up 53 socks every year.

How many socks is this to the nearest ten? ....

Q3   Round the following to the nearest thousand:

a) 2906 ....

b) 2096 ....

c) 5632 ....

d) 4500 ....

e) 18711 ....

f) 47096 ....

Q4   By the time he is 25 the average fisherman will have been nibbled by 28.72 fish.

a) What is this to the nearest whole number?

....

b) What is this to 1 decimal place?

....

By the time it is 25 the average fish will have nibbled 684.575 fishermen.

c) What is this to 1 decimal place? ....

d) What is this to 2 decimal places? ....

You always round off to the **NEAREST NUMBER**. It's a bit more tricky if it's exactly 1/2 **WAY** between 2 numbers — but then you just round **UP.**

Mental Arithmetic

No calculators!

Q1 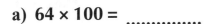 Multiply the following <u>without</u> a calculator.

a) 64 × 100 = ...

b) 11.2 × 1000 = ...

c) 10 × 5.76 = ...

d) 0.083 × 1000 = ...

e) 200 × 342 = ...

f) 50 × 2.8 = ...

Q2 Divide the following <u>without</u> a calculator.

a) 5470 ÷ 10 = ...

b) 251 ÷ 100 = ...

c) 7.2 ÷ 10 = ...

d) 400.9 ÷ 1000 = ...

e) 4800 ÷ 200 = ...

f) 93 ÷ 30 = ...

Q3 Fill in the missing numbers.

a) 27 × .... = 2700

b) .... × 5.3 = 53

c) 4093 ÷ .... = 40.93

d) 10860 ÷ .... = 1086

Q4 George the window cleaner charges £1.49 for each window he cleans. He cleans all 10 windows on Mr Bronson's house.

a) How much will George charge Mr Bronson in total?

....

George takes an average of 10 minutes to clean one window.

b) How much does George charge for each minute of cleaning?

....

Mr Windsor's house is very large, and has 500 windows.

c) How much would it cost Mr Windsor to get George to clean all his windows?

....

Mental Arithmetic

Q5 | Answer these <u>without</u> using a calculator.

a) 1586 + 98 = ...

b) 641 − 96 = ...

c) 199 + 813 = ...

d) 246 + 497 = ...

e) 99 × 7 = ...

f) 4 × 97 = ...

g) 3 × 196 = ...

h) 398 × 5 = ...

Q6 Martha went to her friendly local out-of-town supermarket and bought a fish bowl for £7, a dinosaur egg for £16, and a telephone box for £13.

| Work out <u>in your head</u> how much Martha spent.

....

Q7 | Work out the answers to the following <u>in your head</u>.

a) 15 + 18 + 25 = ...

b) 21 + 7 + 9 = ...

c) 26 + 8 + 22 = ...

d) 13 + 13 + 17 + 17 = ...

Q8 | Answer the following <u>without</u> using a calculator.

a) 9 × 2 × 4 = ...

b) 3 × 8 × 3 = ...

c) 7 × 2 × 3 = ...

d) 2 × 9 × 5 = ...

Q9 Marty drives a total of 198 miles going to and from work each week.

| How far does he drive going to and from work in 6 weeks?

....

Money

Q1

Brian's Fish and Chips — MENU		
Fish and Chips — £2.10	Fish — £1.40	Sausage — 45p
Chips — 70p	Fish Cake — 35p	Curry Sauce — 50p
	Burger — £1.10	

Work out how much each order costs.

a) Two orders of fish and chips ....

b) Fish cake and chips ....

c) Fish and chips and a curry sauce ....

d) Burger and chips ....

e) Sausage and chips ....

f) 2 Fish, 1 burger and 1 curry sauce ....

g) 3 Sausages and a curry sauce ....

h) How much change do you get from £5 for:

i) Two orders of fish and chips ....

ii) Burger and chips ....

iii) Sausage and chips ....

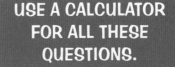

USE A CALCULATOR FOR ALL THESE QUESTIONS.

Q2 A bottle of cola costs £1.24.

Work out the cost of:

a) 10 bottles ....

b) 3 bottles ....

c) 17 bottles ....

Q3 Sausages cost £1.06 per pound.

Work out the cost of:

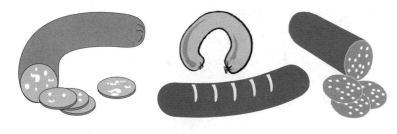

a) 4 pounds ....

b) 5 pounds ....

c) 6.7 pounds ....

Money

Q4

The small bar of chocolate weighs 50g and costs 32p.
The large bar weighs 200g and costs 80p.

a) How many grams do you get for 1p from the small bar?

....

b) How many grams do you get for 1p from the large bar?

....

c) Which bar gives you more for your money?

....

Q5 Fishy Pete the clownfish has two tins
of tuna.

The large tin of tuna weighs 400g and
costs £1.00. The small tin weighs 220g
and costs 60p.

Anyone seen
my scales???

a) How many grams do you get for 1p in the large tin?

....

b) How many grams do you get for 1p in the small tin?

....

c) Which tin gives better value for money?

....

Fractions

Q1 **What fraction is shaded in each of the following pictures?**

a)

b)

c)

....

....

....

d)

e)

f)

....

....

....

Q2 **Shade in the fraction bars below to show each of the given fractions.**

a) $\frac{7}{12}$
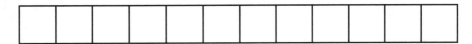

b) $\frac{2}{3}$
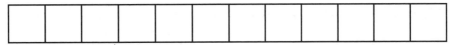

c) $\frac{3}{5}$
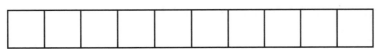

Q3 **Which is bigger?**

a) $\frac{1}{5}$ or $\frac{1}{10}$ ....

b) $\frac{3}{7}$ or $\frac{6}{21}$ ....

c) $\frac{10}{15}$ or $\frac{4}{6}$ ....

d) $\frac{1}{3}$ or $\frac{33}{10}$ ....

Q4 **Work out the following quantities...**

a) Half of 12 = ...

b) Third of 30 = ...

c) $\frac{3}{4}$ of 60 = ...

d) Quarter of 24 = ...

e) $\frac{1}{4}$ of 44 = ...

f) $\frac{2}{3}$ of 6 = ...

Fractions

Q5 Put the following lists of fractions into the correct order, starting with the smallest...

a) $\frac{4}{7}$, $\frac{6}{7}$, $\frac{3}{7}$, $\frac{1}{7}$

b) $\frac{1}{2}$, $\frac{2}{3}$, $\frac{4}{5}$, $\frac{1}{4}$

....

....

....

....

....

....

....

....

Q6 Maurice has made 13 litres of nutritious toothpaste soup, which he plans to share equally between himself and his four best friends, whether they want any or not.

a) How many litres of soup will each person get? Use a fraction in your answer.

....

One of Maurice's friends had to leave before the soup was served.

b) Now how many litres of soup does each person get in total? Use a fraction in your answer. ....

c) Rewrite your answers to parts a) and b), using decimals instead of fractions. ....

Q7 Gwendoline has 27 tonnes of jam. She gives exactly one-sixth to Lucinda.

a) How much jam does she give to Lucinda? Use a fraction in your answer. ....

b) How much jam will Gwendoline have left? Give your answer as a decimal.

....

Percentages

Q1 Shade the correct percentage of each of the pictures below.

a) Shade 60% of the pyramid.

b) Shade 90% of the apples.

c) Shade 30% of the star.

d) Shade 40% of the tower.

e) Shade 25% of the honeycomb.

Q2 Try these without a calculator.

a) 50% of £12 = ...

b) 25% of £20 = ...

c) 10% of £50 = ...

d) 5% of £50 = ...

e) 30% of £50 = ...

f) 75% of £80 = ...

g) 10% of 90cm = ...

h) 10% of 4.39kg = ...

no calculators!!

You can use a calculator for the rest of these questions.

i) 8% of £16 = ...

j) 15% of £200 = ...

k) 12% of 50 litres = ...

l) 85% of 740kg = ...

m) 40% of 40 minutes = ...

n) $17\frac{1}{2}$% of £180 = ...

Percentages

Q3   A rabble of 750 Vikings have been set adrift in rubber dinghies.

a)   If 56% of the Vikings have beards,
what percentage don't?

....

b)   **How many bearded Vikings are there?**

....

c)   6% of the Vikings have fallen in.
How many Vikings is this?   ....

d)   54% of the Vikings can swim, 38% can't swim
but have arm-bands, and the rest sink like
cannonballs.

How many will sink if all the boats capsize?   ....

Q4   **Convert the following percentages to fractions:**

a) 19%   ....   b) 67%   ....   c) 49%   ....

d) 80%   ....   e) 24%   ....   f) 45%   ....

Q5   **Convert these fractions to percentages:**

a) $\dfrac{8}{200}$ ....   b) $\dfrac{22}{50}$ ....   c) $\dfrac{93}{150}$ ....   d) $\dfrac{35}{250}$ ....

Q6   Ronnie Hood and Wilbur Tell are practising archery.
$\dfrac{182}{200}$ of Ronnie's arrows and $\dfrac{267}{300}$ of Wilbur's arrows hit the target.

a)   **Who had the bigger percentage of arrows on target?**

....

b)   **What percentage of his arrows were on target?**   ....

Estimating Fractions and Percentages

Q1 This picture shows three friends who have been painting a wall.
Use the picture to answer the questions below.

Amy   Larry   Anastasia

a) Estimate what <u>fraction</u> of the wall Anastasia has painted.   ....

b) Estimate what <u>fraction</u> of the wall Amy has painted.   ....

c) Estimate what <u>percentage</u> of the wall Larry has painted.   ....

Q2 Rene made a pencil sandwich and a hammer sandwich from a long baguette.

a) Estimate the <u>percentage</u> of the baguette Rene made into a hammer sandwich.   ....

b) Estimate what <u>fraction</u> of the baguette Rene made into a pencil sandwich.   ....

Q3 Joe, Freda and Destiny went out for pizza. They ordered a pizza with three different toppings, which is shown in the picture.

a) Estimate what <u>fraction</u> of the pizza is topped with socks.   ....

b) Estimate the <u>percentage</u> of the pizza that is topped with lolly sticks.   ....

Ratio and Proportion

Q1 Wolfgang has just finished painting the sign below.

SPORT SUPPORTER SUPERSTORE

a) What proportion of the
letters on the sign are black?

1·2

12   12
24

b) What proportion of the
letters on the sign are white?

c) What is the ratio of black letters to white letters?

d) What is the ratio of letter Us to letter Ps?

e) What proportion of the letters on the sign are Rs?

f) What proportion of the letters on the sign are Ts?

Vowels are the letters A, E, I, O and U. Consonants are all the other letters.

g) What is the ratio of vowels to consonants on the sign?

Q2 The picture shows the different cans of healthy fizzy drinks that are
included in each variety pack of 6 cans sold by Vegi-Soda Ltd.

a) What proportion of the cans
in each pack are Carrotade?

b) What proportion of the cans
in each pack are Beetrootade?

Cordelia bought some Vegi-Soda variety packs.
She bought a total of 48 cans.

c) How many cans of Beetrootade did Cordelia buy?

d) How many cans of Carrotade did she buy?

Multiples

Q1 **Find the first five multiples of:**

a) 4 ....

b) 7 ....

c) 12 ....

d) 18 ....

Q2 **Find a number which is a multiple of:**

a) 2 and 6 ....

b) 7 and 5 ....

c) 2 and 3 and 7 ....

d) 4 and 5 and 9 ....

Q3

a) **Find a number which is a multiple of 3 and 8** ....

b) **Find another number which is a multiple of 3 and 8** ....

c) **Find yet another number which is a multiple of 3 and 8** ....

Q4 **Which of these numbers 14, 20, 22, 35, 50, 55, 70, 77, 99 are multiples of:**

a) 2 ....

b) 5 ....

c) 7 ....

d) 11 ....

Factors

Remember that factors are just numbers that divide into another number.

Q1 These are the hands of aliens. Their hands have a times sum on each finger, which for each alien always have the same answer. Since each species of alien has a different answer, they can be called by these numbers:

Species 8   Species 12   Species 7

When Mildew & Scary found the following Aliens they had all their fingers but were missing their factor sums.

Write in each sum and the alien species number.

Species ___   Species 30   Species ___

Q2 The numbers on each finger are known as factors and are usually, on Earth, written as a list. List the factors of the following numbers. Write each factor once, with no repeating.

a) 18 ....

b) 22 ....

c) 35 ....

d) 7 ....

e) 16 ....

f) 49 ....

g) 48 ....

h) 31 ....

i) 50 ....

j) 62 ....

k) 81 ....

l) 100 ....

Prime Numbers and Factors

Q1 Circle each of the prime numbers in this list:

1   3   7   8   15   17   22   27   36   39   41   46   49   51

Q2 Explain how you can tell 28655 isn't a prime number, just by looking at its last digit.

....

....

Q3 Fill in the missing numbers on this factor tree:

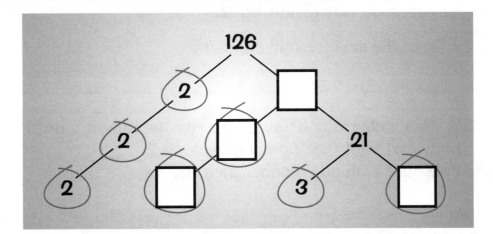

Q4 Write the following numbers as products of prime factors:

a) 24   ....

b) 36   ....

c) 80   ....

d) 78   ....

e) 180   ....

f) 275   ....

Q5 I am thinking of a number.
It is less than 20.
It is an odd number.
It has two different prime factors.

What number am I thinking of?   ....

Even and Odd Numbers

Q1 Look at the list of the counting numbers from 1 to 20. Circle the numbers that divide by 2. Put a box around the numbers that do not divide by 2.

1   2   3   4   5   6   7   8   9   10

11   12   13   14   15   16   17   18   19   20

Even numbers divide by **2**.

Make a list of the next ten even numbers.

....

Odd numbers do not divide by **2**.

Make a list of the next ten odd numbers.

....

Q2 Look at the number bug below. Can you see how it grows?
If the body part is an even number divide by 2.
If the body part is an odd number then add 1.

Now fill in the numbers on the body parts using the two rules above.

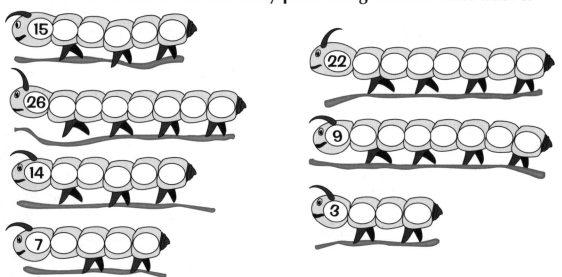

Number Patterns and Sequences

Q1 Draw the next picture in each pattern.
How many match sticks are used in each picture?

a)

....

b)

....

c)

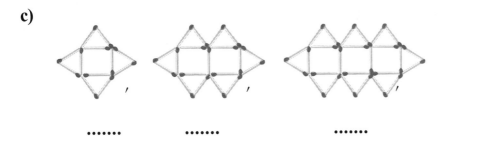

....

Q2 In each of the questions below, write down the next three numbers in the sequence and write the rule that you used to find them.

a) 1, 3, 5, 7, ..., ..., ... Rule ....

b) 3, 7, 11, 15, ..., ..., ... Rule ....

c) 0.3, 3, 30, 300, ..., ..., ... Rule ....

d) 1, 4, 9, 16, ..., ..., ... Rule ....

e) 6, 15, 24, 33, ..., ..., ...

Rule ....

f) 320, 160, 80, 40, 20...... , 11..... , ...

Rule ....

Word Formulae and Equations

Q1   Mrs Jones works out the weekly pocket money for each of her children. She uses the formula:

Pocket money = Age in years × 20 (in pence)

Work out the pocket money for:

a)   Joe, aged 10 years ....

b)   Paul, aged 8 years ....

c)   Sara, aged 5 years ....

Q2   The formula to work out the cooking time for a medium sized sailing boat is:

Cooking time = Number × 32
   (in mins)   of crew

How long will it take to cook a boat with:

a)   a crew of 10 ....

b)   a crew of 15 ....

Q3   The number 32 in the formula above refers to the weight of the boat in tonnes. The full word formula can be written like this:

Cooking time = Number × Weight
   (in mins)   of crew   of boat

Can you work out the cooking times of the following...

a)   a 10 tonne boat with a crew of 10 ....

b)   a 15 tonne boat with a crew of 12 ....

c)   an 8 tonne boat with a crew of 5 ....

Angles

These are two protractors used to measure angles:

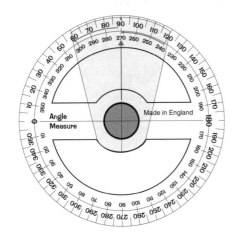

Q1 **Use a protractor to help you to draw the following angles:**

a) **20°**   b) **65°**   c) **90°**

hey, who you calling cute?

d) **Draw an acute angle and measure it.**

e) **Draw an obtuse angle and measure it.**

Acute angle measures ....°   Obtuse angle measures ....°

Angles

Q2 For each of the angles below write down its name, estimate its size (before you measure it!) and finally measure each angle with a protractor.

The first one has been done for you.

Angle	Name	Estimated Size	Actual Size
a	acute	40^0	43^0
b	....	....	....
c	....	....	....
d	....	....	....
e	....	....	....
f	....	....	....

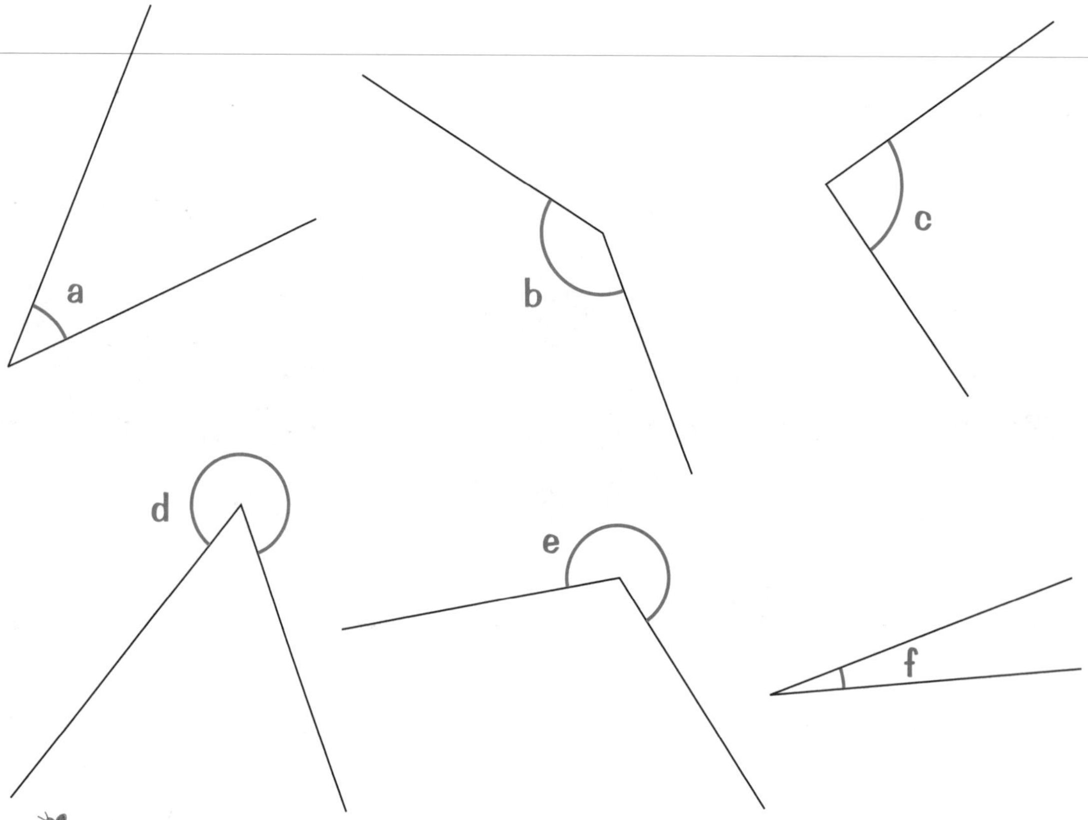

a

b

c

d

e

f

Shapes

Q1 Fill in the blanks in the table.

NAME	DRAWING	DESCRIPTION
Square		Sides of equal length. Opposite sides parallel. Four right angles.
....		Opposite sides parallel and the same length. Four right angles.
....		Opposite sides are .... and Equal. Opposite angles are equal.
Trapezium		Only .... sides are parallel.
Rhombus		A parallelogram but with all sides ....
Kite		Two pairs of adjacent equal sides.

Q2 Draw a trapezium that's different from the one in the table.

Shapes

Q3 Join up the diagrams with the description. One has been done for you.

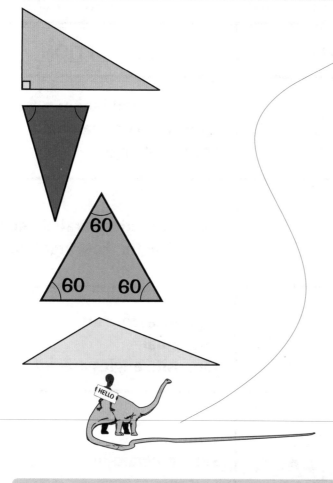

An alien riding a dinosaur

SCALENE Triangle

EQUILATERAL Triangle

RIGHT-ANGLED Triangle

ISOSCELES Triangle

Q4 Fill in the missing shapes or names. The first one has been done for you.

a) **Ivan the** Irregular Polygon

b) **Harry the Hexagon.**

c) **Olive the** ....

d) **Peter the Pentagon.**

e) **Hilda the**

....

Perimeter

Q1 **Work out the perimeters of the following shapes:**

a) **Square Perimeter = ...cm**

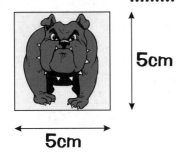

5cm

5cm

b) **Rectangle Perimeter =**
(2 × ......) + (2 × ......) = ...m

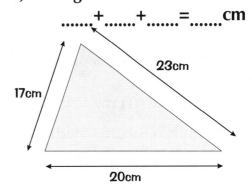

6m

14m

c) **Equilateral Triangle**
Perimeter = 3 × .... = ...cm

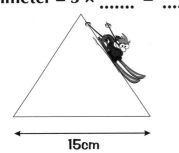

15cm

d) **Triangle Perimeter=**
.......+.......+.......=.......cm

17cm

23cm

20cm

e) **Symmetrical Five-Sided Polygon Perimeter**

= ....+.......+.......+.......+....... = ...cm

12cm

6cm

8cm

f) **Symmetrical Four-Sided Polygon Perimeter**

= ....+.......+.......+.......

= ....m

8.5m

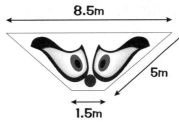

5m

1.5m

Q2

a) **A square field has sides of 10m.**

How much fencing is needed to go around it? **...........m.**

b) **A photo measures 17.5cm by 12.5cm.**

What is the total length of the edges of the photo? **...........cm.**

Areas

Q1 Calculate the area of this composite shape:

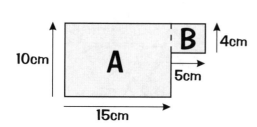

Shape A: length = ... width = ...

Area = ... × .... = ... cm²

Shape B: length = ... width = ...

Area = ... × .... = ... cm²

Total (area A + area B) = ... + ... = ... cm²

Q2 Calculate the areas of the following rectangles:

a) Length = 10 cm, Width = 4 cm,   Area = ... × ..... = ... cm².

b) Length = 55 cm, Width = 19 cm, Area = ... cm².

c) Length = 12 m,   Width = 7 m,   Area = ... m².

d) Length = 155 m, Width = 28 m,   Area = ... m².

e) Length = 3.7 km, Width = 1.5 km, Area = ... km².

Q3 Little Trevor here has kindly stepped on a piece of graph paper leaving his footprint. Each square represents 1cm².

Estimate the area of his footprint by counting the squares that are more than half inside it:

Area .... cm²

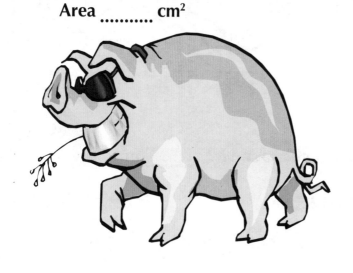

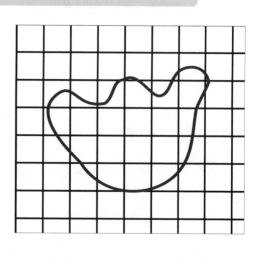

Symmetry

Q1   These shapes have only one line of symmetry.

Draw the line of symmetry using a dotted line.

a)

b)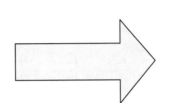

c)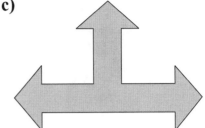

Q2   These shapes have more than one line of symmetry.

Draw the lines of symmetry using dotted lines.

a)

b)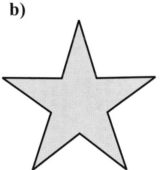

c)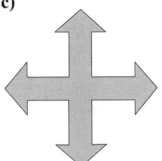

Q3   Some of the letters of the alphabet have lines of symmetry.

Draw the lines of symmetry using a dotted line.

A B C D E F G H I

J K L M N O P Q R

S T U V W X Y Z

Q4   Some of the counting numbers have a line of symmetry.

Draw the line of symmetry using a dotted line.

0 1 2 3 4 5 6 7 8 9

SECTION THREE — SHAPES AND SOLIDS

Reflection

Q1 Draw the reflection in the mirror line.

a)

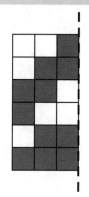

b)

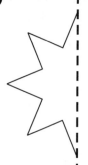

c)

Q2 a) Reflect the word so that the X-axis is the line of symmetry.
b) Reflect the word so that the Y-axis is the line of symmetry.

a)

COMPUTER

X-axis

b)

Y-axis

MOUSE

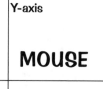

Q3 The blue line represents a line of reflectional symmetry.

Draw the reflected pictures and label the points: A′ B′ C′ D′

a)

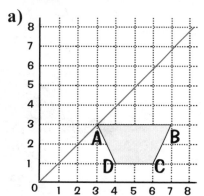

b)

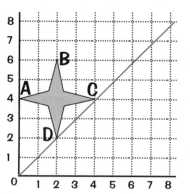

c)

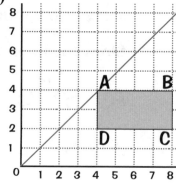

a) **What are the coordinates of:** A′(   ) B′(   ) C′(   ) D′(   )

b) **What are the coordinates of:** A′(   ) B′(   ) C′(   ) D′(   )

c) **What are the coordinates of:** A′(   ) B′(   ) C′(   ) D′(   )

Translation

Q1 Draw the following translations of the shape ABCD on the grid below:

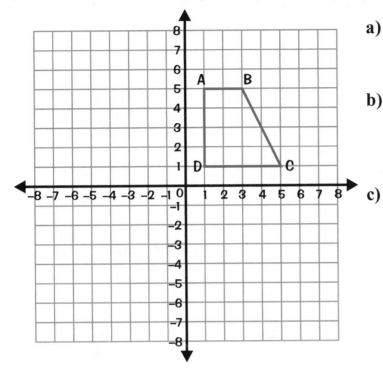

a) Translate ABCD 8 squares down.
Label the points E, F, G and H.

b) Translate ABCD 6 squares to the left.
Label the points K, L, M and N.

c) Translate ABCD 2 squares up and 2 squares to the right.
Label the points W, X, Y and Z.

d) What are the coordinates of: E(   )   F(   )   G(   )   H(   )

e) What are the coordinates of: K(   )   L(   )   M(   )   N(   )

f) What are the coordinates of: W(   )   X(   )   Y(   )   Z(   )

Q2

a) Which of triangles B, C and D is a translation of A?

....

b) Describe the translation used to move triangle A to the triangle you named in part a).

....
....
....

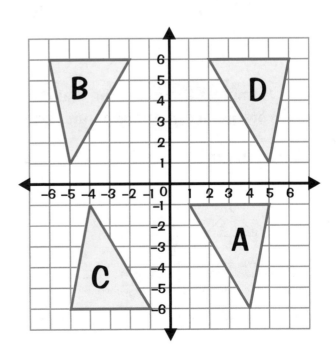

Rotation

Q1 Write down the order of rotational symmetry of each of the following shapes:

a) .... b) .... c) .... d) ....

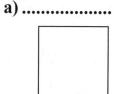

square

rectangle

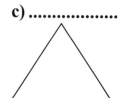

equilateral
triangle

parallelogram

Q2 What is the order of rotational symmetry of the following capital letters?

a) .... b) .... c) .... d) ....

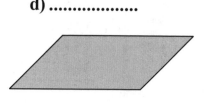

Q3 Find the order of rotational symmetry for the following shapes:

a) .... b) .... c) .... d) ....

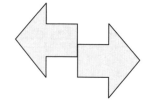

Q4 Complete the following diagrams so that they have rotational symmetry about centre C of the order stated:

a) order 2   b) order 4   c) order 3

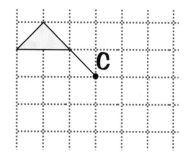
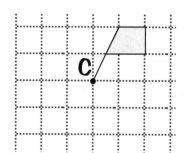
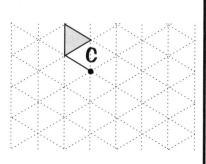

3-D Shapes

Q1   Fill in the boxes in the table.

	Name of SHAPE	number of FACES (SIDES)	number of EDGES	number of VERTICES (CORNERS)

Q2   What are the names of these shapes?

a) ....

b) ....

c) ....

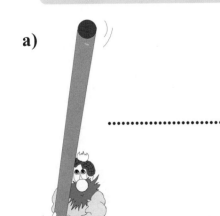

38

Shape Nets

Q1 Which of the following nets would make a cube?

a)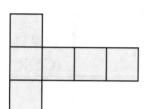

b)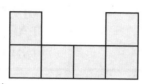

c)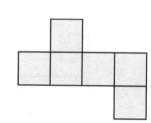

d)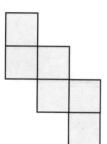

e)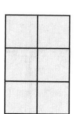

f)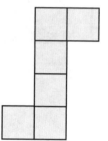

Q2 On a 6-sided dice, opposite numbers should add up to 7.

Fill in the rest of the dots on this net:

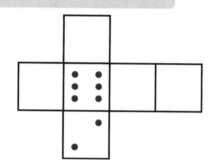

Q3 Which of the nets below would make a square-based pyramid?

a)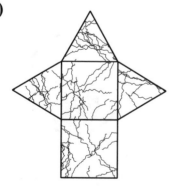

b)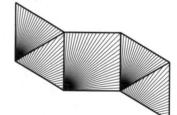

c)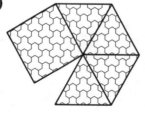

SECTION THREE — SHAPES AND SOLIDS

Coordinates

Q1 Fill in the coordinates of the four points shown:

A (.... , ...)
B (.... , ...)
C (.... , ...)
D (.... , ...)

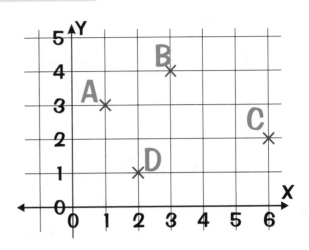

Q2 Mark the following coordinates on the graph (remembering to label them):

Millom (3,1)
Foxfield (5,3)
Beanthwaite (1,1)
Broughton (2,2)

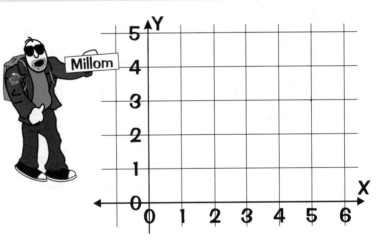

Q3 Add two more points to the graph to produce a kite.
Then write down the coordinates for each.

A (....,....)
B (....,....)
C (....,....)
D (....,....)

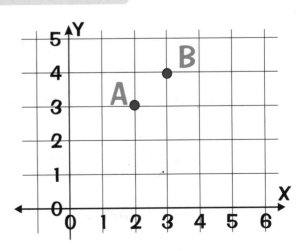

Time

Q1 Complete the following facts about time.

1 day = ... hours.

1 hour = ... minutes.

1 minute = ... seconds.

Q2 Fill in the missing times.

The first one has been done for you

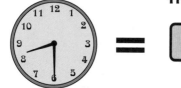 = 8:30 PM = 20:30

= [ ] = 22:25

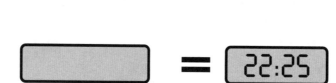 = 11:15 PM = [ ]

= PM = [ ]

Q3 Work out the following times:

How long is it from 7.30am to 11.35am? ....hours............minutes.

How long is it from 8.45am to 12.15pm? ....hours............minutes.

How long is it from 1.10am to 11.25pm? ....hours............minutes.

Units

METRIC UNITS

| km | m | cm | mm | tonne | kg | g | mg | l | ml |

Q1 Which metric units from the box would you use to measure these in?

a) The length of your bedroom ....

b) Your mass ....

c) The distance to Paris ....

d) The amount of water in the bath ....

e) The mass of four racing snails ....

f) The length of your finger ....

g) The amount of medicine in a teaspoon ....

h) The thickness of a coin ....

i) The mass of a bus ....

j) The mass of a triceratops ....

IMPERIAL UNITS

miles, yards, feet, inches, tons, stones, pounds, ounces, gallons, pints

Q2 Which imperial unit goes in the gap? Choose from the box.

a) Paul's mother had a baby today. He weighs about 7 ....

b) A bottle of milk contains 1 ....

c) Sarah is 15 years old. She weighs about 8 ....

d) The distance from Madrid to Barcelona is 311 ....

e) Jane's father is 6 .... tall.

f) This page is nearly 12 .... long.

Bye!

Unit Conversions

APPROXIMATE CONVERSIONS		
1 kg = 2.2 lbs	1 gallon = 4.5 l	1 in = 2.5 cm
1 litre = 1.75 pints		5 miles = 8 km

Q1 The table shows the distances in miles between four towns in Scotland.

Fill in the blank table with the equivalent distances in kilometres.

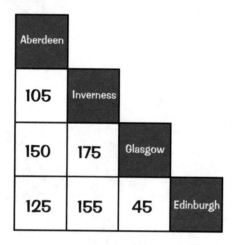

Q2 Change each mass from kilograms to pounds.

10 kg = ... lbs   16 kg = ... lbs   75 kg = ... lbs

Change each of these capacities in gallons to litres.

5 gallons = ... l   14 gallons = ... l   40 gallons = ... l

Q3 Convert the measurements of the caterpillar and pencil to centimetres.

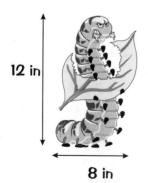

12 ins = ... cm

8 ins = ... cm

5 ins = ... cm

Unit Conversions

SOME USEFUL METRIC CONVERSIONS	
10 mm = 1 cm	1000 mg = 1 g
100 cm = 1 m	1000 g = 1 kg
1000 m = 1 km	1000 ml = 1 l

Q4 **Complete this crossnumber using the conversion factors above.**

ACROSS
1) 2 cm to mm
2) 3500 cm to m
4) 1.02 m to cm
5) 0.5 kg to g
6) 6.7 km to m
7) 890 000 g to kg

DOWN
1) 2.4 m to cm
2) 3 l to ml
3) 5.2 kg to g
4) 1.57 g to mg
6) 69 000 ml to l

Q5 **Fill in the gaps using the conversion factors:**

a) 20 mm = ... cm   .... mm = 6 cm

b) 142 cm = ... m   250 mm = ... cm

c) 9000 m = ... km   .... m = 2 km

d) 3 km = ... m   .... m = 0.5 km

e) 6200 mg = ... g   2.3 kg = ... g

f) 12 000 g = ... kg   7.5 kg = ... g

g) 1.2 l = ... ml   4400 ml = ... l

Unit Conversions

Q6 This graph shows the exchange rate between British pounds (£) and Moon dollars (M$).

How many Moon dollars would I get for:

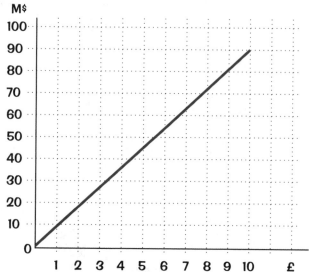

a) £10 ....

b) £4 ....

c) £8 ....

Q7 How many British pounds would I get for:

a) M$ 70 ....

b) M$ 20 ....

c) M$ 5 ....

Q8 This graph can be used to convert the distance (miles) travelled in a taxi to the fare payable (£).

How much will the fare be if you travel:

a) 2 miles ....

b) 5 miles ....

c) 6 miles ....

How far could you travel if you paid:

d) £5 ....

e) £11 ....

f) £7 ....

Reading Scales

Q1 Write down the mass of the following items:

a)

b)

c)

.....................g

.....................kg

.....................pounds

Q2 Give your answers to the following to the nearest centimetre.

a) **How tall is the juggling alien?**

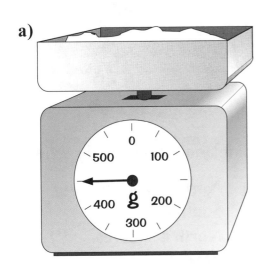

.....................cm

b) **How tall is his keyboard-playing brother?**

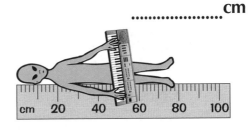

.....................cm

Q3 How much liquid is in the measuring jug?

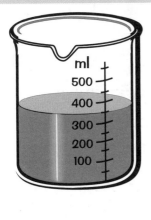

.....................ml

Q4 How much juice has Alex squeezed out of his calculator?

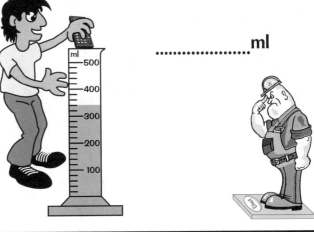

.....................ml

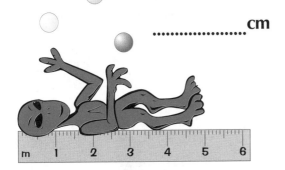

Compass Directions

Q1

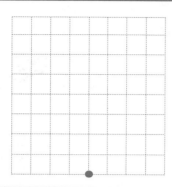

Start at the dot in the middle of the bottom line and follow the directions.

a) West 4 squares.
b) North 4 squares.
c) East 4 squares.
d) South 4 squares.
e) North East through 2 squares.
f) North 4 squares.
g) South West through 2 squares.
h) West 4 squares.
i) North East through 2 squares.
j) East 4 squares.

What shape have you drawn? ....

Q2

Joe's house

Shop

Church

Sue's house

Park

Jane's house

a) What direction does Jane go to get to Sue's house? ....

b) What direction is the church from Joe's house? ....

c) What is South East of Sue's house? ....

d) What is West of Sue's house? ....

e) Jane is at home. She is going to meet Sue in the park. They are going to the shop and then to Joe's house.

Write down Jane's directions.

....

Tables and Tally Marks

Tally charts are really simple — and they make sure you don't miss out any items. Worth doing, you've got to admit.

Q1   At the Swedish Motor Show 60 people were asked what type of vehicle they preferred. Lars wrote down their replies using a simple letter code.

Saloon - S   Hatchback - H   4x4 - F   Milk float - M   Robin Reliant - R

Here is the full list of replies.

H	S	R	S	S	R	M	F	S	S	R	R
M	H	S	H	R	H	M	S	F	S	M	S
R	R	H	H	H	S	M	S	S	R	H	H
H	H	R	R	S	S	M	M	R	H	M	H
H	S	R	F	F	R	F	S	M	S	H	F

Fill in the tally table and add up the frequency in each row.

TYPE OF CAR	TALLY	FREQUENCY
Saloon		
Hatchback		
4 × 4		
Milk float		
Robin Reliant		

Q2   Last year Beanthwaite's strawberry picking bonanza lasted 32 days. During the 32 days the number of strawberries lost each day to Owen (the monster snail) were recorded as shown.

```
2   4   3   5   1   0   0   1   1   0   4   1   0   3   2   1
1   1   0   3   1   1   4   2   1   2   1   3   2   0   0   2
```

Complete the tally chart and add up the frequency in each row.

Straw-berries	TALLY	FREQUENCY
0		
1		
2		
3		
4		
5		

Graphs and Charts

Q1 This bar chart shows the marks from a test taken by some students:

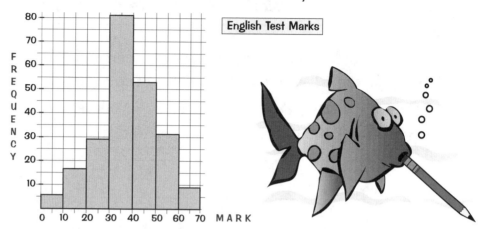

a) How many students scored 20 marks or less? ....

b) The pass mark for this test was 30.

How many students passed the test? ....

c) How many students took the test? ....

Q2 This pictogram shows the favourite drinks of a group of pupils.

Favourite Drinks	Number of Pupils
Lemonade	✦ ✦ ✦ ✦ ✦ ✦ ✦ ✦ ✦
Mango Juice	✦ ✦ ✦ ✦ ✦ ✦ ✦ ✦ ✦ ✦ ✦
Milk	✦ ✦ ✦ ✦ ✦ ✦
Orange Squash	✦ ✦ ✦
Blood	✦

✦ Represents 2 pupils.

a) How many pupils were questioned? .... pupils.

b) How many pupils don't prefer a fizzy drink? .... pupils.

c) How many pupils are vampires? .... pupils.

d) 18 pupils liked lemonade best. How many more liked mango juice best?

.... pupils.

e) Make one general comment about the information given.

....

Graphs and Charts

Q3 The pictogram shows the number of people buying bicycles during a 5 year period.

Year	Number of people buying bikes
2002	🚲 🚲
2003	🚲 🚲 🚲
2004	🚲 🚲 🚲 🚲 🚲
2005	🚲 🚲 🚲 🚲 🚲 🚲 🚲
2006	🚲 🚲 🚲 🚲 🚲 🚲 🚲 🚲

🚲 **Represents 8000 people**

a) **How many people bought bikes during these 5 years?** .... people.

b) **How many people bought bikes in the last 2 years of the period?**

.... people.

c) **How many more people bought bikes in 2006 than in 2002?**

.... people.

Q4 Here is a horizontal bar chart showing the favourite colours of a class of pupils.

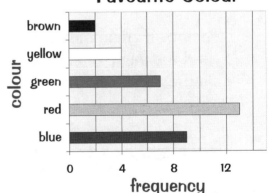

Favourite Colour

a) **How many like blue best?** ....

b) **How many like brown best?** ....

c) **How many pupils took part in this survey?** ....

d) **What fraction of the class prefer green?** ....

e) **What fraction of the class like red or blue best?** ....

Graphs and Charts

Q5 Complete this frequency table, and then draw a bar chart for the results:

TEST SCORE	TALLY	FREQUENCY
1 - 5	卌 l	6
6 - 10	卌 lll	
11 - 15	lll	
16 - 20	卌	
21 - 25	lll	

F
R
E
Q
U
E
N
C
Y

TEST SCORE

Q6 A chef spends £540 each week on various items which are listed in the table and shown as sectors on the pie chart.

Using an angle measurer or by calculation find the angle of each sector and enter it in the table.

Item	£	Angle
Beans	150	
Frogs' Legs	30	
Potatoes	90	
Rats' Tails	30	
Spinach	45	
General	195	

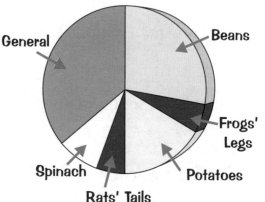

Understanding Data

Discrete data can be counted exactly, so it's always whole numbers. Continuous data can't be measured exactly, so you can write it to any number of decimal places.

Q1 Chloe and Audrey are making a scientific study of wild sofas in Scotland.

Are the following examples of continuous data or discrete data?

a) Audrey measures the heights of all the sofas. ....

b) Chloe records how fast each sofa can run. ....

c) Chloe counts how many flying sofas there are. ....

d) Audrey finds the weight of each sofa. ....

e) Chloe records how many sofas are more than 6 metres long. ....

Q2 The two graphs show the number of visitors to the National Toadstool Museum for three years.

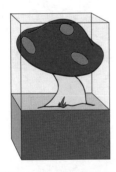

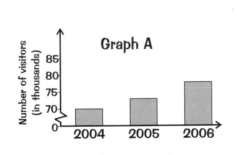

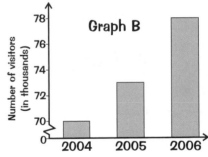

a) Which graph makes it look like the number of visitors was increasing more quickly? ....

b) Explain why one graph makes it look like the number of visitors was increasing more quickly?

....

....

....

Mean

Q1 **Find, <u>without</u> a calculator, the mean for each of these sets of data:**

a) 5, 3, 7, 3, 2 = ...

b) 18, 6, 12, 4 = ...

c) 7, 3, 9, 5, 3, 5, 4, 6, 2, 6 = ...

d) 5, 4, 0, 3, 0, 6 = ...

Q2 **Now you can use a calculator to find the mean.**
If necessary, round your answers to 1 decimal place:

a) 13, 15, 11, 12, 16, 13, 11, 9 = ...

b) 16, 13, 2, 15, 0, 9 = ...

c) 80, 70, 80, 50, 60, 70, 90, 60, 50, 70, 70 = ...

Q3 The beautiful Emily measured the heights of her five
friends. The measurements in metres were:

1.65, 1.66, 1.70, 1.72, 1.67

What was the mean height of her friends?

....

Q4 Stephen scored a mean mark of 64 in four Maths tests.

a) **What was his total mark for all four tests?**

....

When he did the next test, he managed 74.

b) **What was his mean mark after the fifth test?**

....

Mode

Q1 **Find the MODE for each of these sets of data.**

a) 3, 5, 8, 6, 3, 7   Mode is ....

b) 52, 26, 13, 52, 31, 26, 13, 52, 87, 41   Mode is ....

Q2 The temperatures in °C on 10 summer days in England were:

  25, 18, 23, 19, 23, 24, 23, 18, 20, 19

What was the modal temperature?   Modal temperature ....°C.

Q3 The first 30 entrants in a competition were given an envelope with a sum of money in it. The amounts were:

  £5,   £10,   £5,   £1,   £20,   £20,   £10,   £5,   £10,   £20
  £10,   £20,   £10,   £5,   £10,   £5,   £10,   £10,   £5,   £20
  £1,   £5,   £10,   £5,   £20,   £1,   £20,   £10,   £5,   £10

What was the modal amount?   Modal amount £ ....

Q4 20 dominoes were picked at random and for each the number of dots was added to give a score. The dominoes picked were:

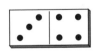

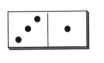

What was the modal score?   Modal Score ....

Median

Q1 **Find the median for these sets of data:**

a) 3,   6,   7,   12,   2,   5,   4,   2,   9

.... Median is ....

b) 14,   5,   21,   7,   19,   3,   12,   2,   5

.... Median is ....

Q2 The teachers at Grim Hill school were made to take a Maths test. Here are their scores out of 100.

62	1	74	48	52
19	67	34	27	63
49	34	58	32	46

What is the median result?   **Fill in the shaded box.**

														Median

Q3 Some information about the seven members of the famous pop group 'Unleaded Budgie' is shown below.

Height	145cm	156cm	159cm	346cm	42cm	154cm	161cm
Weight	87kg	83kg	85kg	989kg	86kg	90kg	88kg
Age	43	54	42	237	46	58	51

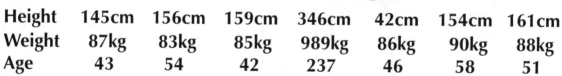

Fill in the table below:

Median Height	Median Weight	Median Age

Range

Q1 The number of goals scored by a hockey team over a period of 10 games is listed below.

0, 3, 2, 4, 1, 2, 3, 4, 1, 0.

What is the range of number of goals? ....

Q2 Sarah and her friends were measured and their heights were found to be:

1.52m, 1.61m, 1.49m, 1.55m, 1.39m, 1.56m.

What is the range of the heights? ....

Q3 Here are the times six people took to do a Maths test:

1 hour 10 mins, 2 hours 50 mins, 1 hour 35 mins,
1 hour 55 mins, 1 hour 18 mins, 2 hours 15 mins.

What is the range of these times? ....

Q4 The number of cornflakes packets sold on 5 days were:

8pkts, 3pkts, 15pkts, 9pkts, 4pkts.

What is the range of packets? ....

Q5 **What is the range in the number of letters contained in each of the words in this question?**

....

Q6 Some friends compared their pocket money. The least amount was 40p a week and the range was £3.10p.

How much was received by the person who got the most? ....

Q7 The weights of some people were surveyed. The heaviest person was 70kg and the range of weights was 11kg.

What was the weight of the lightest person? ....

Probability

Q1 Write down if each of these events is impossible, unlikely, even chance, likely or certain.

a) You will go shopping on Saturday.

....

b) You will live to be 150 years old.

....

c) A card picked at random from a normal pack of 52 cards will be a red card.

....

d) The day after next Monday will be Tuesday.

....

Q2 Match up the events from the lists below into pairs that are equally likely. One has been done for you.

Rolling a 6 on a fair dice.

Rolling an even number on a fair dice.

A banana being elected Prime Minister.

Rolling a 1 on a fair dice.

Rolling less than 10 on a fair dice.

Finding Henry VIII hiding behind your curtains.

Getting heads when you toss a normal coin once.

Getting wet if you fall in the sea.

Q3 Decide how likely the following events are. Number them from 1 to 5, with 1 the most likely and 5 the least likely.

.... Rolling a number that isn't 3 on a normal dice.

.... An ice lolly melting if you leave it in the sun all day.

.... Rolling an odd number on a normal dice.

Excuse me, do you know the way to the fish and chip shop?

.... A talking cat asking you for directions on the way home.

.... Choosing the jack of diamonds when you pick one card at random from a normal pack.

Key Stage 2 Maths Workbook Answers

Number Stuff

Page 1
Q1 a) 26   b) 73
   c) 860   d) 5792
   e) 27052   f) 4114
   g) 314.00, 42673.29

Q2 a) twenty-seven
   b) five hundred and seven
   c) three thousand, eight hundred and twenty-four
   d) sixty-three thousand, four hundred and ninety-two
   e) two hundred and forty-five thousand and ninety-four
   f) three hundred and seventy-two thousand six hundred and three

Page 2
Q3 a) 197, 372, 450, 463, 612, 804
   b) 75, 86, 402, 553, 2123, 3860
   c) 1680, 1724, 1726, 1797, 1832, 1879

Q4   21454, 21295, 21071, 21056, 18704, 18659, 18468, 18237

Adding

Page 3
Q1 a) 14   b) 39
   c) 106   d) 294
   e) 701   f) 2726

Q2 a) 95   b) 123   c) 724

Q3 a) 52   b) 29   c) 69

Q4   1283   894   745   2922
     29   42   54   125

Subtracting

Page 4
Q1 a) 23   b) 22
   c) 65   d) 17
   e) 38   f) 53
   g) 452   h) 216
   i) 327   j) 536
   k) 583   l) 333
   m) 537   n) 452

Q2 a) 17   b) 80
   c) 120   d) 75
   e) 164   f) 969

Q3   177

Q4   365m

Negative Numbers

Page 5
Q1   -10 -9 -8 -7 -6 -5 -4 -3 -2 -1 | 1 2 3 4 5 6 7 8 9 10 11

Q2 a) -11, -9, -8, -2, -1
   b) -10, -9, -7, -4, -2, 1, 13
   c) -19, -12, -8, -5, 0, 2, 6, 12

Q3 a) 150 °C
   -50   0   50   100
   b) 44 °C
   -18   0   26

Multiplication

Page 6
Q1 a) 240   b) 1431

Q2 a) 46   b) 120
   c) 212   d) 65
   e) 100   f) 126
   g) 65   h) 162
   i) 375   j) 372
   k) 1232   l) 2475
   m) 1730   n) 1716

Division

Page 7
Q1 a) 10   b) 7
   c) 10   d) 3
   e) 5   f) 6
   g) 45   h) 333
   i) 80   j) 31
   k) 62   l) 22
   m) 60   n) 54
   o) 49

Q2 a) £137 344   b) £34336
   c) £14848   d) 1073 pairs

Using Calculations

Page 8
Q1 a) 9 × **32** = 288   b) 213 × **4** = 852
   c) **261** × 3 = 783   d) 7 × **481** = 3367

Q2 a) 7   b) 15   c) 4

Q3 a) 5   b) 9   c) 60
   d) 3   e) 9   f) 36

Decimals

Page 9
Q1 a) 2.7   b) 14.8
   c) 20.9   d) 33.2

Q2 a) 0.1   b) 0.3
   c) 0.5   d) 0.8

Q3   Philip

Q4   Lisa

Q5 a) 177.8cm   b) 144.8cm

Rounding Off

Page 10
Q1 a) £400   b) £800
   c) £700   d) £1700
   e) £100   f) £0

Q2   50

Q3 a) 3000   b) 2000
   c) 6000   d) 5000
   e) 19000   f) 47000

Q4 a) 29   b) 28.7
   c) 684.6   d) 684.58

Mental Arithmetic

Page 11
Q1 a) 6400   b) 11200
   c) 57.6   d) 83
   e) 68400   f) 140

Q2 a) 547   b) 2.51
   c) 0.72   d) 0.4009
   e) 24   f) 3.1

Q3 a) 100   b) 10
   c) 100   d) 10

Q4 a) £14.90   b) £0.149 (or 14.9p)
   c) £745

Page 12
Q5 a) 1684   b) 545
   c) 1012   d) 743
   e) 693   f) 388
   g) 588   h) 1990

Q6   £36

Q7 a) 58   b) 37
   c) 56   d) 60

Q8 a) 72   b) 72
   c) 42   d) 90

Q9   1188 miles

Money

Page 13
Q1 a) £4.20   b) £1.05
   c) £2.60   d) £1.80
   e) £1.15   f) £4.40
   g) £1.85
   h) i) £0.80   ii) £3.20   iii) £3.85

Q2 a) £12.40   b) £3.72   c) £21.08

Q3 a) £4.24   b) £5.30   c) £7.10

Page 14
Q4 a) 1.56g   b) 2.5g   c) larger one

Q5 a) 4g   b) 3.66g   c) larger one

Fractions

Page 15
Q1 a) $\frac{1}{4}$ b) $\frac{3}{8}$ c) $\frac{4}{10} = \frac{2}{5}$
   d) $\frac{2}{10} = \frac{1}{5}$ e) $\frac{3}{7}$ f) $\frac{5}{18}$

Q2 a) 7 of the 12 boxes should be shaded
   b) 8 of the 12 boxes should be shaded
   c) 6 of the 10 boxes should be shaded

Q3 a) $\frac{1}{5}$ b) $\frac{3}{7}$ c) same   d) $\frac{33}{10}$

Q4 a) 6   b) 10   c) 45
   d) 6   e) 11   f) 4

Key Stage 2 Maths Workbook Answers

Page 16

Q5 a) $\frac{1}{7}, \frac{3}{7}, \frac{4}{7}, \frac{6}{7}$ b) $\frac{1}{4}, \frac{1}{2}, \frac{2}{3}, \frac{4}{5}$

Q6 a) $2\frac{3}{5}$ b) $3\frac{1}{4}$

   c) 2.6, 3.25

Q7 a) $4\frac{1}{2}$ tonnes (or $4\frac{3}{6}$ tonnes)

   b) 22.5 tonnes

Percentages

Page 17

Q1 a) 6 of the 10 boxes should be shaded
   b) 9 of the 10 apples should be shaded
   c) 3 of the 10 triangles should be shaded
   d) 2 of the 5 boxes should be shaded
   e) 5 of the 20 hexagons should be shaded

Q2 a) £6   b) £5
   c) £5   d) £2.50
   e) £15   f) £60
   g) 9 cm   h) 0.439 kg
   i) £1.28   j) £30
   k) 6 litres   l) 629 kg
   m) 16 mins   n) £31.50

Page 18

Q3 a) 44%   b) 420
   c) 45   d) 60

Q4 a) $\frac{19}{100}$ b) $\frac{67}{100}$

   c) $\frac{49}{100}$ d) $\frac{80}{100} \left(= \frac{4}{5}\right)$

   e) $\frac{24}{100} \left(= \frac{6}{25}\right)$

   f) $\frac{45}{100} \left(= \frac{9}{20}\right)$

Q5 a) 4%   b) 44%
   c) 62%   d) 14%

Q6 a) Ronnie   b) 91%

Estimating Fractions and Percentages

Page 19

Q1 a) about $\frac{1}{2}$ b) about $\frac{3}{10}$

   c) about 20%

Q2 a) about 75%   b) about $\frac{1}{4}$

Q3 a) about $\frac{1}{3}$ b) about 25%

Ratio and Proportion

Page 20

Q1 a) 1 in every 2   b) 1 in every 4
   c) 2 to 1   d) 2 to 4, or 1 to 2
   e) 5 in every 24   f) 1 in every 8
   g) 1 to 2

Q2 a) 1 in every 2   b) 1 in every 3
   c) 16   d) 24

Multiples

Page 21

Q1 a) 4, 8, 12, 16, 20
   b) 7, 14, 21, 28, 35
   c) 12, 24, 36, 48, 60
   d) 18, 36, 54, 72, 90

Q2 a) e.g. 6   b) e.g. 35
   c) e.g. 42   d) e.g. 180

Q3 a) e.g. 24   b) e.g. 48   c) e.g. 72

Q4 a) 14, 20, 22, 50, 70
   b) 20, 35, 50, 55, 70
   c) 14, 35, 70, 77
   d) 22, 55, 77, 99

Factors

Page 22

Q1 1×18, 2×9, species 18.
   3×10, 5×6, 2×15, species 30.
   4×4, 1×16, species 16.

Q2 a) 1, 2, 3, 6, 9, 18   b) 1, 2, 11, 22
   c) 1, 5, 7, 35   d) 1, 7
   e) 1, 2, 4, 8, 16   f) 1, 7, 49
   g) 1, 2, 3, 4, 6, 8, 12, 16, 24, 48
   h) 1, 31   i) 1, 2, 5, 10, 25, 50
   j) 1, 2, 31, 62   k) 1, 3, 9, 27, 81
   l) 1, 2, 4, 5, 10, 20, 25, 50, 100

Prime Numbers and Factors

Page 23

Q1 3, 7, 17, 41

Q2 It ends in 5, so it divides by 5.
   All primes apart from 2 and 5 end in 1, 3, 7 or 9.

Q3 Missing numbers:
   Second row — 63
   Third row — 3
   Bottom row — 3, 7

Q4 a) $2 \times 2 \times 2 \times 3$
   b) $2 \times 2 \times 3 \times 3$
   c) $2 \times 2 \times 2 \times 2 \times 5$
   d) $2 \times 3 \times 13$
   e) $2 \times 2 \times 3 \times 3 \times 5$
   f) $5 \times 5 \times 11$

Q5 15

Even and Odd Numbers

Page 24

Q1 Circles: 2, 4, 6, 8, 10, 12, 14, 16, 18, 20
   Boxes: 1, 3, 5, 7, 9, 11, 13, 15, 17, 19
   Even numbers:
   22, 24, 26, 28, 30, 32, 34, 36, 38, 40
   Odd numbers:
   21, 23, 25, 27, 29, 31, 33, 35, 37, 39

Q2 <u>15</u>, 16, 8, 4, 2, 1
   <u>26</u>, 13, 14, 7, 8, 4, 2, 1
   <u>14</u>, 7, 8, 4, 2, 1
   <u>7</u>, 8, 4, 2, 1
   <u>22</u>, 11, 12, 6, 3, 4, 2, 1
   <u>9</u>, 10, 5, 6, 3, 4, 2, 1
   <u>3</u>, 4, 2, 1

Number Patterns and Sequences

Page 25

Q1 a) 4,7,10,13
   b) 3,5,7,9
   c) 12,19,26,33

Q2 a) 9,11,13   odds
   b) 19, 23, 27   add 4
   c) 3000,30000,300000   times by 10
   d) 25, 36, 49   square numbers
   e) 42,51,60   add 9
   f) 20,10,5   half previous

Word Formulae and Equations

Page 26

Q1 a) £2   b) £1.60   c) £1.00

Q2 a) 320 mins   b) 480 mins

Q3 a) 100 mins   b) 180 mins   c) 40 mins

Angles

Page 27

Q1 a)   b)   c)

   d) 0-90°   e) 90° - 180°

Page 28

Q2 b) obtuse, 143°   c) right, 90°
   d) reflex, 301°   e) reflex, 248°
   f) acute, 16°

Key Stage 2 Maths Workbook Answers

Shapes
Page 29

Q1 rectangle, , parallelogram,

parallel, 2, equal, 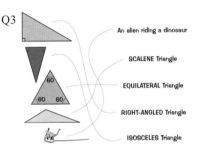.

Q2 e.g.

Page 30

Q3

An alien riding a dinosaur

SCALENE Triangle

EQUILATERAL Triangle

RIGHT-ANGLED Triangle

ISOSCELES Triangle

Q4 b) ⬡ c) Octagon d) ⬠

  e) Heptagon

Perimeters
Page 31

Q1 a) 20cm b) 40m

  c) 45cm d) 60cm

  e) 44cm f) 20m

Q2 a) 40m b) 60cm

Areas
Page 32

Q1 170cm²

Q2 a) 40cm² b) 1045cm²

  c) 84m² d) 4340m²

  e) 5.55km²

Q3 16cm²

Symmetry
Page 33

Q1 a) b) c)

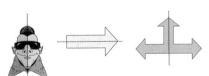

Q2 a) b) c)

Q3 A B C D E F
G H I J K L
M N O P Q R
S T U V W X
Y Z

Q4 0 1 2 3 4
5 6 7 8 9

Reflection
Page 34

Q1 a) 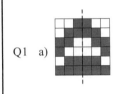 b)

c)

Q2 a)
COMPUTER   X-axis
COMPUTER

b)   Y-axis
MOUSE | MOUSE

Q3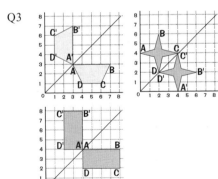

a) (3, 3) (3, 7) (1, 6) (1, 4)
b) (4, 0) (6, 2) (4, 4) (2, 2)
c) (4, 4) (4, 8) (2, 8) (2, 4)

Translation
Page 35

Q1 a), b), c)

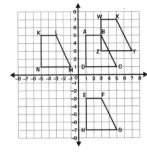

  d) (1, –3) (3, –3) (5, –7) (1, –7)
  e) (–5, 5) (–3, 5) (–1, 1) (–5, 1)
  f) (3, 7) (5, 7) (7, 3) (3, 3)

Q2 a) D

  b) A is translated right 1 unit
     and up 7 units.

Rotation
Page 36

Q1 a) 4 b) 2

  c) 3 d) 2

Q2 a) 2 b) 1

  c) 2 d) 1

Q3 a) 2 b) 3

  c) 2 d) 1

Q4 a) 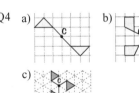 b)

  c)

3-D Shapes
Page 37

Q1 cube - 6,12,8

  cuboid - 6,12,8

  triangular prism - 5,9,6

  pyramid - 5,8,5

Q2 a) cylinder b) cone c) sphere

Shape Nets
Page 38

Q1 a) yes b) no c) yes
  d) yes e) no f) yes

Q2

  (or with 3 and 4 the other way round)

Q3 a) no b) yes c) no

Key Stage 2 Maths Workbook Answers

Coordinates

Page 39

Q1   A(1,3); B(3,4) ; C(6,2); D(2,1).

Q2

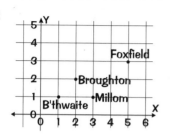

Q3   (2, 3)   (3, 4)   (4, 3)   (3, 1)

Time

Page 40

Q1   24, 60, 60

Q2   10:25 PM,   23:15,   9:00,   21:00

Q3   4,5   3,30   22,15

Units

Page 41

Q1   a) m/cm   b) kg
     c) km   d) l
     e) g   f) mm/cm
     g) ml   h) mm
     i) tonne   j) tonne

Q2   a) pounds   b) pint
     c) stone   d) miles
     e) feet   f) inches

Unit Conversions

Page 42

Q1

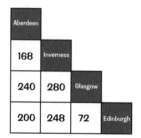

Q2   a) 22, 35.2, 165, 22.5, 63, 180

Q3   30, 20, 12.5

Page 43

Q4

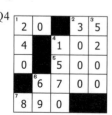

Q5   a) 2, 60   b) 1.42, 25
     c) 9, 2000   d) 3000, 500
     e) 6.2, 2300   f) 12, 7500
     g) 1200, 4.4

Page 44

Q6   a) 90   b) 36   c) 72

Q7   a) 7.78   b) 2.22   c) 0.56

Q8   a) £5   b) £9.50   c) £11
     d) 2 miles   e) 6 miles   f) 3.33 miles

Reading Scales

Page 45

Q1 a) 450 g   b) 15 kg   c) 625 pounds

Q2 a) 500 cm   b) 78 cm

Q3 350 ml

Q4 340 ml

Compass Directions

Page 46

Q1 A cube

Q2 a) NW   b) SW
   c) Jane's House
   d) The Church
   e) NE, NW, W

Tables and Tally Marks

Page 47

Q1 S = 17, H = 15, F = 6, M = 9, R = 13

Q2 0 = 7, 1 = 11, 2 = 6, 3 = 4, 4 = 3, 5 = 1

Graphs and Charts

Page 48

Q1 a) 23   b) 175   c) 227

Q2 a) 60   b) 42   c) 2   d) 4
   e) Odd sample - Mango juice most
      popular and no mention of cola

Page 49

Q3 a) 200 000   b) 120 000
   c) 48 000

Q4 a) 9   b) 2   c) 35
   d) 1/5   e) 22/35

Page 50

Q5

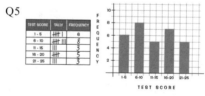

Q6 B. = 100°   F.L. = 20°
   P. = 60°   R.T. = 20°
   S. = 30°   G. = 130°

Understanding Data

Page 51

Q1 a) continuous   b) continuous
   c) discrete   d) continuous
   e) discrete

Q2 a) graph B
   b) The vertical scale on graph B is
   more stretched out than on graph A,
   and has smaller intervals between its
   marks. This makes the differences
   between the heights of the bars bigger.

Mean

Page 52

Q1 a) 4   b) 10   c) 5   d) 3

Q2 a) 12.5   b) 9.2   c) 68.2

Q3 1.68 m

Q4 a) 256   b) 66

Mode

Page 53

Q1 a) 3   b) 52

Q2 23 °C

Q3 £10

Q4 7

Median

Page 54

Q1 a) 5   b) 7

Q2 1, 19, 27, 32, 34, 34, 46, 48, 49, 52,
   58, 62, 63, 67, 74. Median = 48

Q3 Median Height = 156 cm
   Median Weight = 87kg
   Median Age = 51 years

Range

Page 55

Q1 4

Q2 0.22 m

Q3 1 hr 40 mins

Q4 12 pkts.

Q5 7

Q6 £3.50

Q7 59 kg

Probability

Page 56

Q1 a) Depends on pupil
   b) unlikely
   c) evens
   d) certain

Q2 Pairs:
   Rolling a 6 on a fair dice, and rolling a
   1 on a fair dice.
   Rolling less than 10 on a fair dice, and
   getting wet if you fall in the sea.
   Getting heads when you toss a normal
   coin once, and rolling an even number
   on a fair dice.

Q3 2, 1, 3, 5, 4